GW01086899

Play your Ocarina

Songs of Praise

'Ocarina Songs of Praise' First published 2001 **ISBN 1 871210 19 4**
'Ocarina Songs of Praise' **CD edition** First published 2006 **ISBN 1 871210 31 3**

All contents and musical arrangements copyright © 2001 David and Christa Liggins,
Ocarina Workshop, PO Box 56, Kettering, NN15 5LX, UK.

Give me oil in my lamp

Verse 1: Give me oil in my lamp, keep me burn - ing.___

Give me oil in my lamp, I pray.

Give me oil in my lamp, keep me burn - ing,___

Keep me burn - ing 'til the break of day.

2 Give me joy in my heart, keep me singing . . .

3 Give me love in my heart, keep me serving . . .

4 Give me peace in my heart, keep me resting . . .

Chorus: Sing ho - san - na, sing ho - san - na,

Sing ho - san - na to the King of Kings!

Sing ho - san - na, sing ho - san - na,

Sing ho - san - na to the King!

Play a descant to the chorus with one long note per bar like this:

Sing _____ Sing _____ Sing _____ King _____

Sing _____ Sing _____ Sing _____ King _____

3

Colours of day

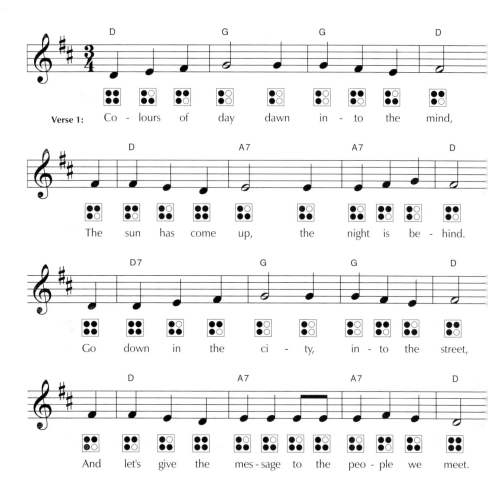

Verse 1: Co - lours of day dawn in - to the mind,

The sun has come up, the night is be - hind.

Go down in the ci - ty, in - to the street,

And let's give the mes - sage to the peo - ple we meet.

2 Go through the park, on into the town;
The sun still shines on, it never goes down.
The light of the world is risen again,
The people of darkness are needing our friend . . .

3 Open your eyes, look into the sky,
The darkness has come, the sun came to die.
The evening draws on, the sun disappears,
But Jesus is living, his spirit is near . . .

4 Words and music: Sue McClellan, John Paculabo and Keith Rycroft copyright © 1974 Thankyou Music / Adm. by
worshiptogether.com. songs excl. UK & Europe, adm. by kingswaysongs.com tym@kingsway.co.uk. Used by permission.

Chorus: So light up the fire and let the flame burn,
O - pen the door, let Je - sus re - turn.
Take seeds of his spi - rit, let the fruit grow,
Tell the peo - ple of Je - sus, let his love show.

To add group harmonies in the Chorus:
Play lines 3 and 4 as a harmony to lines 1 and 2.
Play lines 1 and 2 as a harmony to lines 3 and 4.

One more step

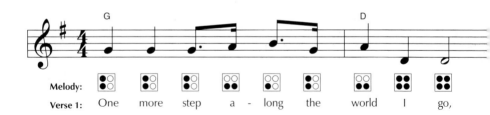

Melody:

Verse 1: One more step a - long the world I go,

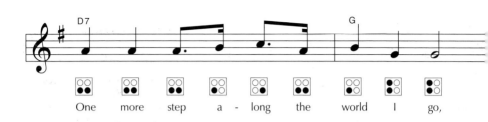

One more step a - long the world I go,

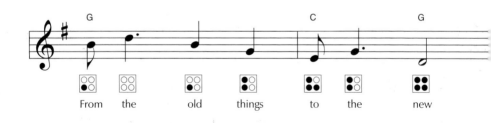

From the old things to the new

2 Round the corners of the world I turn,
   More and more about the world I learn.
   And the new things that I see
   You'll be looking at along with me . . .

3 As I travel through the bad and good
   Keep me travelling the way I should.
   Where I see no way to go
   You'll be telling me the way I know . . .

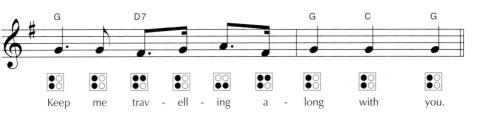

Keep me trav - ell - ing a - long with you.

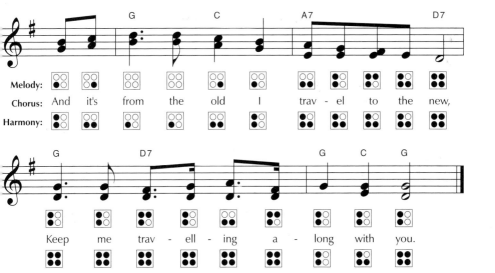

Melody:

Chorus: And it's from the old I trav - el to the new,

Harmony:

Keep me trav - ell - ing a - long with you.

4 Give me courage when the world is rough,
Keep me loving though the world is tough.
Leap and sing in all I do,
Keep me travelling along with you . . .

5 You are older than the world can be
You are younger than the life in me.
Ever old and ever new,
Keep me travelling along with you . . .

The wise man built his house upon the rock

Verse 1: The wise man built his house up - on the rock,___

The wise man built his house up - on the rock,___

Melody: The wise man built his house up - on the rock

Harmony:

And the rain came tum - bling down.___

Play E# in the first line by repeating
F# and half-covering the open hole
(see inside back cover).

And the rain came down and the floods came up,

The rain came down and the floods came up,

Melody: The rain came down and the floods came up

Harmony:

And the house on the rock stood firm.

2 The foolish man built his house upon the sand,
The foolish man built his house upon the sand,
The foolish man built his house upon the sand,
And the rain came tumbling down.

And the rain came down and the floods came up,
The rain came down and the floods came up,
The rain came down and the floods came up,
And the house on the sand fell flat.

Kumbaya

2 Someone's crying, Lord, Kumbaya . . .

3 Someone's singing, Lord, Kumbaya . . .

4 Someone's praying, Lord, Kumbaya . . .

Praise him, praise him

2. Trust him, trust him . . .

3. Serve him, serve him . . .

4. Praise him, praise him . . .

Thank you for my friends

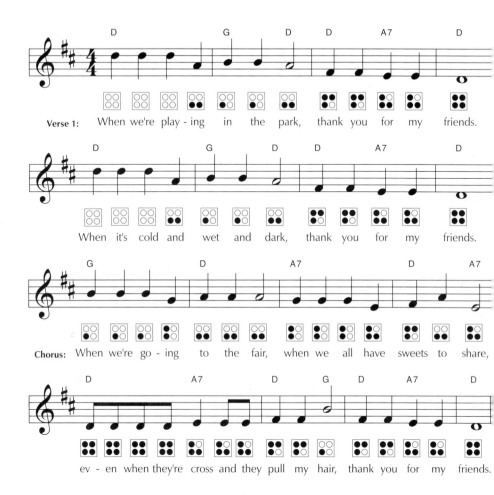

Verse 1: When we're play-ing in the park, thank you for my friends.

When it's cold and wet and dark, thank you for my friends.

Chorus: When we're go-ing to the fair, when we all have sweets to share,

ev-en when they're cross and they pull my hair, thank you for my friends.

2 When I'm feeling very sad, thank you for my friends. (clap, clap)
  When I'm feeling cross and bad, thank you for my friends. (clap, clap) . . .

3 When I have a birthday tea, thank you for my friends. (clap, clap)
  When I fall and cut my knee, thank you for my friends. (clap, clap) . . .

4 When we play our special games, thank you for my friends. (clap, clap)
  When they scowl and call me names, thank you for my friends. (clap, clap) . . .

When I needed a neighbour

Verse 1: When I need-ed a neigh-bour were you there, were you there?

When I need-ed a neigh-bour were you there?

And the creed and the co - lour and the

Name won't mat - ter, were you there?

2 I was hungry and thirsty, were you there, were you there? . . .

3 I was cold, I was naked, were you there, were you there? . . .

4 When I needed a shelter, were you there, were you there? . . .

5 When I needed a healer, were you there, were you there? . . .

6 Wherever you travel, I'll be there, I'll be there? . . . I'll be there.

On a 4-hole ocarina, play B instead of the 6-hole note above.

Words and music: Sydney Carter © 1971 Stainer & Bell Ltd. London, UK. Used by permission.
Tune title: Neighbour.

Make me a channel of your peace

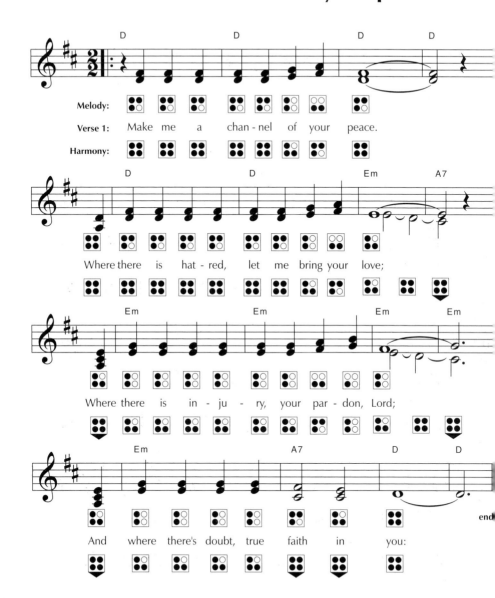

2 Make me a channel of your peace.
   Where there's despair in life, let me bring hope;
   Where there is darkness, only light;
   And where there's sadness, ever joy: . . .

Words and music: Sebastian Temple, dedicated to Mrs Frances Tracy © 1967 OCP Publications,
5536 NE Hassalo, Portland, OR 97213, USA. All rights reserved. Used with permission.

Chorus: Oh, Mas - ter, grant that I may nev - er seek_____

So much to be con - soled as to con - sole;_____

To be un - der - stood as to un - der - stand;_____

To be loved, as to love with all my soul._____

3 Make me a channel of your peace.
It is in pardoning that we are pardoned,
In giving to all men that we receive,
And in dying that we're born to eternal life.

Lord of the dance

Melody:

Verse 1: I danced in the morn - ing when the world was be - gun,

Harmony:

And I danced in the moon and the stars____ and the sun;

And I came down from hea - ven and I danced on the earth;

At Beth - le - hem I had my birth.

2 I danced for the scribe and the pharisee,
  But they would not dance and they wouldn't follow me.
  I danced for the fishermen, for James and John –
  They came with me and the dance went on . . .

3 I danced on the Sabbath and I cured the lame;
  The holy people said it was a shame.
  They whipped and they stripped and they hung me on high,
  And they left me there on a cross to die . . .

4 I danced on a Friday when the sky turned black;
 It's hard to dance with the devil on your back.
 They buried my body and they thought I'd gone –
 But I am the Dance, and I still go on . . .

5 They cut me down and I leapt up high;
 'I am the life that'll never, never die.
 I'll live in you if you'll live in me;
 I am the Lord of the Dance.' said he . . .

See him lying on a bed of straw

2 Star of silver, sweep across the skies,
   Show where Jesus in the manger lies;
   Shepherds, swiftly from your stupor rise
   To see the Saviour of the world! . . .

3 Angels, sing again the song you sang,
   Sing the glory of God's gracious plan;
   Sing that Bethlehem's little baby can
   Be the Saviour of us all . . .

Words and music: Michael Perry © Mrs B Perry / Admin. by The Jubilate Group,
4 Thorne Park Road, Torquay, TQ2 6RX, UK. copyrightmanager@jubilate.co.uk Used by Permission.

Chorus: O now car - ry me to Beth - le - hem _____
To see the Lord _____ of love a - gain: _____
Just as poor _____ as was the sta - ble then, _____
The prince of glo - ry when he came.

4 Mine are riches, from your poverty,
From your innocence, eternity;
Mine, forgiveness by your death for me,
Child of sorrow for my joy . . .

On a 4-hole ocarina, play B instead of the 6-hole notes above.

Little donkey

Melody:

Verse 3: Lit - tle don - key, lit - tle don - key, had a hea - vy day

Harmony:

Lit - tle don - key, car - ry Ma - ry safe - ly on her way.

repeat chorus & verse 3

Playout: Lit - tle don - key, car - ry Ma - ry safe - ly on her way.

Who built the ark?

2 He built it long, both wide and tall,
Plenty of room for the large and small . . .

3 He found him and axe, and hammer too,
Began to cut and began to hew . . .

4 And every time that hammer ring,
Noah shout and Noah sing . . .

He's got the whole world

1 He's got the wind and the rain in his hand, (x 3)
   He's got the whole world in his hand . . . Chorus:

2 He's got the sun and the moon in his hand, (x 3) . . .

3 He's got the plants and the creatures in his hand, (x 3) . . .

4 He's got everybody here in his hand, (x 3) . . .

Who put the colours in the rainbow?

Verse 1:
Who put the co-lours in the rain-bow? Who put the salt in-to the sea?
Who put the hump up-on the cam-el? Who put the neck on the gi - raffe?

Who put the cold in-to the snow-flake? Who made you and me?
Who put the tale up-on the mon-key? Who made hy-e-nas laugh?

Melody:
Chorus: Who made whales and snails and quails? Who made hogs and dogs and frogs?
Harmony:

Who made bats and rats and cats? Who made ev-'ry - thing?

2 Who put the gold into the sunshine? Who put the sparkle in the stars?
Who put the silver in the moonlight? Who made Earth and Mars?
Who put the scent into the roses? Who taught the honey bee to dance?
Who put the tree inside the acorn? It surely can't be chance! . . .

Words and music: J P Booth copyright © Paul Booth administered by CopyCare,
PO Box 77, Hailsham, BN27 3EF, UK. Used by permission. music@copycare.com

Think of a world without any flowers

Verse 1: Think of a world with - out an - y flow - ers, Think of a world with - out an - y trees, Think of a sky with - out an - y sun - shine, Think of the air with - out an - y breeze. We thank you, Lord, for flow'rs and trees and sun - shine, We thank you, Lord, and praise your ho - ly name.

2 Think of a world without any animals, think of a field without any herd,
   Think of a stream without any fishes, think of a dawn without any bird.
   We thank you, Lord, for all your living creatures,
   We thank you, Lord, and praise your holy name.

3 Think of a world without any people, think of a street with no-one living there,
   Think of a town without any houses, no-one to love and nobody to care.
   We thank you, Lord, for families and friendships,
   We thank you, Lord, and praise your holy name.

Words: Doreen Newport; music: Graham Westcott; © 1969 & 1973 Stainer & Bell Ltd. London, UK.
Used by permission. Tune title: Genesis.

Autumn days

2 Clouds that look like familiar faces, and a winter's moon with frosted rings,
  Smell of bacon as I fasten up my laces, and the song the milkman sings . . .

3 Whipped-up spray that is rainbow-scattered, and a swallow curving in the sky,
  Shoes so comfy though they're worn-out and battered, and the taste of apple-pie . . .

4 Scent of gardens when the rain's been falling, and a minnow darting down a stream,
  Picked-up engine that's been stuttering and stalling, and a win for my home team . . .

Note: this ocarina version is pitched one note higher than is found in other assembly song-books.

Words and music: Estelle White © 1969 Stainer & Bell Ltd. and McCrimmon Publishing Company Ltd.
Used by permission.

Cauliflowers fluffy

Verse 1: Caul - i - flow - ers fluf - fy and cab - ba - ges green,

Straw - ber - ries___ sweet - er than an - y I've seen,

Beet - root pur - ple and on - ions white: All grow stead - i - ly day and night.

Chorus: The ap - ples are ripe, the plums are red,

Broad beans are sleep - ing in a blank - et - y bed._____

2 Blackberries juicy and rhubarb sour, marrows fattening hour by hour,
   Gooseberries hairy and lettuces fat, radishes round and runner beans flat . . .

3 Orangey carrots and turnips cream, reddening tomatoes that used to be green,
   Brown potatoes in little heaps down in the darkness where the celery sleeps . . .

On a 4-hole ocarina, play A instead of the 6-hole note above.

Words: V P Mitchell; music: H C Mitchell; copyright control.

If I were a butterfly

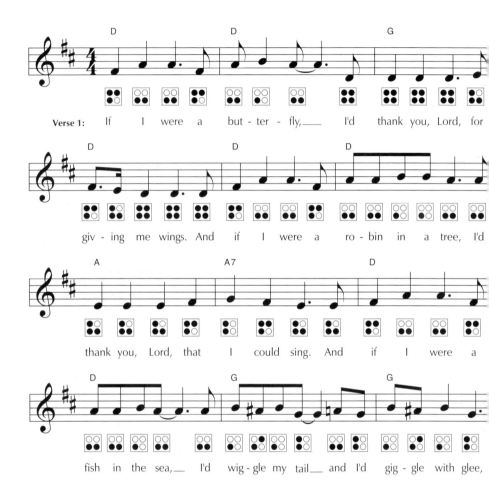

Verse 1: If I were a but-ter-fly,___ I'd thank you, Lord, for giv-ing me wings. And if I were a ro-bin in a tree, I'd thank you, Lord, that I could sing. And if I were a fish in the sea,___ I'd wig-gle my tail___ and I'd gig-gle with glee,

2 If I were an elephant, I'd thank you, Lord, by raising my trunk.
And if I were a kangaroo you know I'd hop right up to you.
And if I were an octopus, I'd thank you, Lord, for my fine looks,
But I just thank you, Father for making me 'me' . . .

3 If I were a wiggly worm, I'd thank you, Lord, that I could squirm,
And if I were a billy goat, I'd thank you, Lord, for my strong throat,
And if I were a fuzzy wuzzy bear, I'd thank you, Lord, for my fuzzy wuzzy hair,
But I just thank you, Father for making me 'me' . . .

Words and music: Brian Howard copyright © 1975 Mission Hills Music, administered by CopyCare, PO Box 77, Hailsham, BN27 3EF, UK. Used by permission. music@copycare.com

But I just thank you, Fa - ther, for mak - ing me 'me'.____

Chorus: For you gave me a heart____ and you gave me a smile,____

You gave me Je - sus and you made me your child,____

And I just thank you, Fa - ther, for mak - ing me 'me'._____

Play E# by repeating F# and half-covering the open hole
(see inside back cover). Alternatively just leave a gap!

Now the green blade rises

2 In the grave they laid him, love whom men had slain,
   Thinking that he never would awake again:
   Laid in the earth like grain that sleeps unseen:
   Love is come again like wheat that springs up green.

3 Forth he came at Easter, like the risen grain,
   He that for the three days in the grave had lain:
   Quick from the dead my risen Lord is seen:
   Love is come again like wheat that springs up green.

4 When our hearts are wintry, grieving or in pain,
   Then your touch can call us back to life again:
   Fields of our heart that dead and bare have been:
   Love is come again like wheat that springs up green.

Peace is flowing like a river

Verse 1: Peace is flow - ing like a ri - ver,

Flow - ing out through you and me,___

Spread - ing out in - to the de - sert,

Set - ting all the peo - ple free.

2 Love is flowing like a river,
  Flowing out through you and me,
  Spreading out into the desert,
  Setting all the people free.

3 Joy is flowing like a river,
  Flowing out through you and me,
  Spreading out into the desert,
  Setting all the people free.

4 Hope is flowing like a river,
  Flowing out through you and me,
  Spreading out into the desert,
  Setting all the people free.

I've got a body

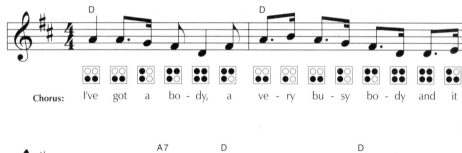

Chorus: I've got a bo-dy, a ve-ry bu-sy bo-dy and it

goes___ ev-'ry-where with me.

Verse 1: And on that bo-dy
2: And on that bo-dy
3: And on that bo-dy

I've got a nose and it goes___ ev-'ry-where with me. And I
I've got some hands and they go___ ev-'ry-where with me. And I
I've got some feet and they go___ ev-'ry-where with me. And I

1a: Sniff sniff here, Sniff sniff there, sniff sniff sniff sniff ev-'ry-where.
2a: Clap clap here, clap clap there, clap clap clap clap ev-'ry-where.
3a: Stamp stamp here, stamp stamp there, stamp stamp stamp stamp ev-'ry-where.

Play, sing and perform actions in this order:
Chorus, 1, 1a; Chorus, 2, 2a 1a;
Chorus, 3, 3a, 2a, 1a; Chorus.